MY BEST DECISION

A Nurse's Journey through School and Career. A Story for Everyone to Read.

By

Kitty R Elers RN BSN

Dedication

I dedicate this book to all nurses – past, present, and future.

In Memory of My Mother C Lorraine Elers and My Father Charles Hugh Elers (Bud), a loving thank you for making my lifelong dream of becoming a nurse possible.

About the Author

Nursing was a second career for Ms. Elers. She made the decision to enter nursing after working unhappily in a brokerage firm. Ms. Elers attended Burdett College, Laboure School of Nursing, and Northeastern University in Boston to achieve her nursing goals. Working as a volunteer has been a very important part of her life. She has volunteered for the Red Cross, Hope Hospice, and Medical Reserve Corp. of Massachusetts (assisting with disasters). Combining nursing and volunteer work enhanced her compassion for caring. Ms. Elers is also a member of the Sigma Theta Tau National Honor Society, NU Chapter.

Introduction

Greetings to all and I hope my book with stories will find a way into the hands of nurses, anybody thinking of entering the nursing profession and everyone else. Nursing was a second career for me. I made the decision to enter nursing school at the age of 28. It was always a lifelong dream. You will understand why I chose the name My Best Decision in the very first chapter. I had worked in a renowned brokerage firm in Boston in the cashier's department, working with cash and stocks and bonds worth millions. I would walk to the Federal Reserve almost daily and make huge deposits while being accompanied with my very own Armed Security Guide.

I missed human contact and working with patients so that is when I made the decision to start taking nursing classes.... Nursing has a huge advantage over many other healthcare fields. You can work in any specialty you choose. My areas were Medical/Surgical in the hospital, Intensive Care Unit, Hemodialysis, Hospice, working with the homeless population, and eventually, entering administration/management. The most challenging positions, I saved for last. I chose to work in another culture in another part of the world for three years in Saudi Arabia. The last ten years of my nursing career were in the prison system running a clinic off hours with inmates in a medium security facility. I loved the job. You are probably wondering why I jumped around so much: it was my choice. I wanted to experience as many aspects of nursing I could. In this book, you will find a spattering of memories I thought would be worth sharing.

Table of Contents

The Fruitfly Story

After almost or over 40 years of nursing, I have decided to share my experiences with the rest of the world. Many of these stories are comical and some are very sad. Many of my friends have stated "Kitty, you really should write down some of these stories, they are really phenomenal." I am trying to think back to when I wanted to "help people".

I was very young around 8 years of age on a hot summer day in my family's living room. I remember seeing a fruitfly or flea from our family pet flying around the window pane. As I looked closer, I noticed it flying off balance. I soon realized it had a leg missing, which looked like a small piece of lint. I felt sad and wanted and needed to do something about this situation right away. It was now stuck, and I soon discovered the missing appendage was stuck on the window sill. I retrieved it with my mother's eyebrow tweezer. I do remember attaching the leg back onto the live little insect and quickly yelled for my mother to come and take a look. She was very optimistic and gave me much support for doing such a wonderful and courageous act and "trying" to save something so small. Of course, my Sunday school classes came to immediate focus. And while I was remembering that we are all God's creatures and loved by God, I very gently picked up the small appendage and placed it on the insect where the missing leg should belong using the tweezers. And to this day, I could not and still cannot believe that it actually attached itself. My mother was just as surprised. I gently put the fruitfly into a jar and made a decision to let it fly away. My memory is perhaps distorted or unclear, but I did "let it go". And was never sure of its outcome. My mother and I were very amazed at what we had just witnessed. But I do remember receiving such praise that day, which gave me a little faith in myself. That day, I made a decision that when I grew up, I would assist any living creature (human or otherwise) to an improved life and eliminate suffering.

After embracing some memories throughout the year, I realize this particular memory was responsible for my devoted efforts of caring for others on a psycho-spiritual and physical level. Throughout the years from 8 to adulthood, I championed always for the underdog. From the schoolboy who lost the fight on the playground to a friend suffering from a broken heart, there were many instances including bruised bodies as well as bruised hearts. I truly felt very comfortable in my "niche" and mostly the appreciation I did receive in return. There were times I felt the need to stand back to wait and see if I was needed. I also received the lesson of allowing others to heal on their own and not to rescue. There were times I felt drained and depressed and soon realized caring is a double-edged sword. Lesson #2 was learning to take care of my own needs and living a balanced life. No, it wasn't always easy. But I know I was put on God's earth to serve and to heal. Now, I would like to share some of my memories. Some are very sad while other instances throughout my nursing career are quite comical.

Jack of All Trades

Now, you might be thinking why did she start nursing at 30 years instead of after high school? Well, I was sidetracked as many were during the end of 60's into the 70's. I know I wanted to work in the medical field but did not know which direction to take. After attending and graduating from a small college in Boston with an AD in business, I ended up at a brokerage firm in the Dividend Department cutting enormous checks to very wealthy people and making huge deposits to the Federal Reserve Bank. Why was I doing this? It seemed I was going in the opposite direction I had intended. The job was great, but I was very unhappy doing it and realized I was not fulfilling my full potential. My high school transcript was not the greatest, and it lacked a lot of the sciences I needed to attend nursing school. I decided to take a Medical Assistant course for 9 months, which at least got me into the medical field and added exposure to people in a medical setting. I loved the course and the jobs I had after graduation. I had exposure to healthcare both in doctor's offices and in a hospital setting. After two years, I needed to grow and challenge myself further. Many of the doctors I worked with at Beth Israel Hospital encouraged me to go further to nursing school and move on. I was exposed to a large variety of procedures in an outpatient setting, such as assisting a neurologist with a lumbar puncture, blood drawing, setting up and performing electrocardiograms, processing patients, assisting the urologist with sperm specimens, and the list goes on and on. But the skills I accomplished were plentiful. I quickly learned that hands on skills and tasks were just a small part of the job. Dealing with many patients daily was a joyous part of the job. I was exposed to happy, angry, fearful, depressed, and sometimes psychotic behaviors, which I had to quickly adjust to. My confidence excelled because I was labeled "a natural". This of course gave me the confidence to move onto nursing school and take those challenging science courses.

The Early Challenges

My biggest challenge was finding a nursing school that would accept the science courses I had taken in order to enter their program. After many interviews, much unhappiness with rejections, I eventually did find a program that allowed me to enter but only after successfully completing chemistry, biology, and pathophysiology on the college level. I entered Northeastern University and Laboure Nursing College and decided to take each course one at a time. It took a little over a year, but my confidence was up, and I managed to pass all of these courses with a B. This allowed me to enter nursing school finally. However, there were still science courses I had to complete. Nursing school was a trip and a half.

Basic nursing 101, I came close to failing. The nursing instructors were very strict. In 101, you are taught the very basics of care, such as handwashing and bed-making. I remember I was the second or third to "show the other" how proper nursing handwashing is done. Well, the instructor did not like the way I washed my hands and I along with one other person out of about 15 had to rewash our hands. I wasn't happy. Pretty much the same situation arose when it came to bed-making. The list went on learning to make an occupied bed, bed bathing, mouthcare, etc. I wasn't sure I made the right decision about nursing, and this was only the first semester!!! Help. Plus, I was taking other courses in science, liberal arts, etc. Fortunately, I had a little financial assistance from my parents. I worked only 8 hours a week at my old job for extra cash. I had to study several hours a day just to keep up. And I was keeping up. But it was not without its challenges. The 2nd semester was not a very smooth one either. Clinically, it was tough. One of the instructors seemed a little too strict and we all had to really buckle down. The preparation for our days on the medical units was nerve racking. I do not know of a soul that slept the night before. Had to rise at 4:30 am to shower, put nursing school uniform on, and have breakfast. Those mornings were always so dark and cold, and there were times I had to pull over the side of the road and vomit because of nerves. It happened twice.

Well, I had to really decide if nursing was for me. I couldn't believe I had gone this far and was ready to call it quits. I kept thinking of the people I would disappoint. My parents, who had given so much emotional support, but especially myself. But, how could I go on, knowing I did not like it and feel so unhappy. One day during lunch, I met with one of the seniors and relayed my inner most insecurities and feelings. She started laughing...which I could not believe. I do not remember her exact words but what was explained to me that this was just the preliminary nursing course, and once I graduated and received enough experience under "my belt", I could go on to very exciting specialties, with travel or management. But it would take some time. I did go on to love nursing school, knowing I did have a future of many choices, but it was not without a "few more bumps along the road" while in school.

There are many stories to tell. One comes to mind. I was assigned a Mrs. Ruth Smith (fictitious) who was a very confused elderly woman in her 80's with pneumonia and urinary tract infection. She was also status post right leg amputation above the knee. My job was to get her out of bed with her prosthesis on after giving her morning care and breakfast. All was ok till I had to get her up. Mrs. Smith was experiencing phantom pain, making my efforts to applying her prothesis impossible. Despite her pain medication, which she had received, the MD said, "No more narcotics". I decided to use my common sense and NOT APPLY the prosthesis since it was generating much emotional and physical pain for the patient. Three of us got her from the bed to the chair without complications and Mrs. Smith appeared to be comfortable watching TV. My instructor walked in for a mid-morning review and was not happy with my assessment and final decision regarding this patient (not applying prosthesis). I was spoken to very harshly despite my reasoning and was given a low grade for that clinical day. I eventually (1 year later) did report this to the director of my nursing program.

This was a huge start for students to step forward and learn to use common sense when giving care to their patients and for nurses to think outside the box. In the early days, many of us were afraid to speak up for what we thought was right. But eventually, you learn to advocate for your patients. I also have to share this story as well. Since I was a student, we had to warn all other healthcare professionals of our status. On the right sleeve of all nursing uniforms was a sewn-on emblem which stated "NURSING STUDENT". My very confused patient (status post stroke) saw the word murder in the word nursing. I guess the N looked like an M and poor Mrs. Brown was convinced I was going to murder her!! Another eventful clinical day!! I never did convince her that I was her student nurse. However, she was able to receive her care.

Well, the stories could go on and on. And, my fellow classmates had much to talk about during our breaks. I often stated "this should be on live TV" because nobody would believe it. It was a live soap opera. The most difficult semester was the 3rd during our freshmen year. The seniors had completed their nursing program and graduated. The halls and library were quieter but the fear and anxiety had markedly increased for the freshmen. The third semester was considered the "weed out" semester. All those who had difficulties were further challenged. We were divided up into smaller groups, each with an instructor. I had Miss Jones (fictitious) and she had a reputation for being a drill sergeant. All we talked about were past stories from previous years, which were spread down to us and embellished in some way. One particular morning, after reviewing my patients chart, diagnosis, and medications till nearly 1 am and up at 4:30 am with very little sleep. I had to pull over the side of the road and vomit because I was so nervous. This was not the first time. We had pre-conference before going up on the clinical units to review and share our individual care plans for our assigned patients. Usually, there were one or two that were further challenged with additional questions. We all had our turn of humiliation. Somehow, we all got through it and survived. One particular episode comes to mind, early one clinical morning in the hospital cafeteria: As you know, all nursing students wear a uniform and cap which sets us apart from the floor staff RN's. Along with wearing white hose and white shoes, our caps had to be properly placed with bobby pins, which were not to be seen. This particular morning, I guess I was a little careless. As I was standing in line, I felt a soft thump on the side of my head. At first, I thought someone had accidently bumped into me. Well, I was incorrect in my thinking. As I turned around, I saw "Miss Jones" right behind me looking angry stating, "No bobby pins are to be seen". Everyone around me was shocked. All I could hear was OOOHHS and Ahhs. I only remember bending down and picking up my cap. I did continue to stay in the food line, and after having my breakfast, my friends reapplied my cap with no bobby pins in sight. The story quickly spread throughout the school and onto the other programs. As nursing students, we had become so conditioned to expect the unexpected and/or being laid out in front of others that we just adapted knowing it was temporary.

I will mention during this time, it was very difficult for me because my father had become ill with lung cancer and his prognosis was not good. At the time, my older sister was living in California with her husband and young children, and my brother was living in Florida working very hard. My dear mother and I had to cope and I remember deciding to take one day at a time. I do want to mention that these stories are all fact and that the school program was one of the best. There were many kind staff and professors who were approachable. We did have some fun parties and lots of laughs throughout. All this assisted in eliminating our stress levels. There is not one single nursing program known to mankind that is easy. However, let's get back to nursing school. That 3rd semester "weed out" section did finally come to an end. On our last clinical day, we met with our individual instructors. There were about 8 in my group. Since my last name began with an E, I was somewhat near the middle. We were all shaking in our boots, and once again, I was about to vomit but did not. The person before me was taking a very long time and the room was very quiet compared to the previous interviews, and most or all students were in and out with smiles. I waited and waited and several of us were getting concerned. All of a sudden, there was movement with the door opening very slowly. Very sad scene…"Doris" came out with tears and walked to the stairwell avoiding the elevator. She was never seen from again. So, it was true, some do not make it. I felt even worse because I was the one who had to follow that interview. However, my future as a nurse was secured. I even accepted "Miss Jones" apology for thumping my cap off my head that day in the cafeteria. And yes again, there were several who did not make it through that semester. By the time I reached my car, I was walking on clouds. No school, no studying, and no clinical for 10 weeks.

I had secured my parttime job at Beth Israel Hospital as a medical assistant for a summer job, but that too would soon change. As students, we were reminded not to study over the summer as to avoid burnout. They wanted our brains to be fresh and not too tired. I heartily agreed!! My summer started off great with weekends down the cape, working part-time and enjoying life.

By mid-summer, my parents needed me. Dad was not feeling well again and had to go into the hospital for further treatment and Mom at the same time needed knee surgery from a fall. I was needed at home immediately. Both Mom and Dad returned home within 48 hours of each other. I was never so busy trying to organize all their medications, appointments, chemotherapy, physical therapy, food shopping, and etc., along with waiting on them hand and foot. Now, I do not want to sound ungrateful, but I was younger and had other plans for "my summer", which did not happen. I was so busy and the time went by so quickly, before I knew it, it was mid-August and I only had till Labor Day. Both my parents were very resilient and wanted their independence from me. I was turning into Nurse Ratchet. I wanted perfection and was most likely driving them crazy. It was time for me to move back to my studio apartment and get ready for school. When I look back to this very special time, I am very grateful to have had the chance to take care of them. It was a true test of care delivery for me.

More about that Summer

I was given the opportunity to return to my roots. Having left home for school after high school returning for holidays and vacations, I was able to relive my childhood. My bedroom had not changed in ten years. And it was just about 10 years to the day since High School graduation. I renewed many memories, many happy and a few not so happy. Teenage years were a little tough but I came through them and adjusted. I even had the opportunity to ride my childhood bike, and go to the park and play on the swings. A good friend of mine Lucy was also home unexpectedly for the summer, as well. She too, was in her childhood room but with a 6-year-old daughter. Lucy was going through a divorce. We managed to find each other and renew our friendship by "hanging out" and catching up with some old friends. Thank God for Lucy for the summer of 1980. To this day, we are friends and Lucy is a happily remarried grandmother now. The summer was winding down, and I could feel separation anxiety over leaving my home once again. Initially, I felt in a rush to leave but when the time came, I was a little sad realizing that these times were precious and would never be repeated. Once I was back to my apartment closer to the city, I realized I had more responsibilities as a student nurse and more was expected of me. And this scared me. I decided to have one final fun weekend away on Cape Cod with some good friends over Labor Day. We swam, sailed, and partied till 3-4 in the morning because in less than a week, I was to return to studying and face difficult clinical days and stress.

Finally, when school did start, I was ready. This was a year of difficult specific clinical rotations. I decided to start with Psychology or referred to as

Psych Nursing. We were assigned a local Veterans Hospital psych unit in Boston. It turned out to be more challenging than I had anticipated. But, I did learn. We all had the opportunity to choose our own patients and to follow them through for 8 weeks. I chose the patient of least resistance. He was an older veteran with a diagnosis of untreated depression. It turned out to be a violent place, secondary to drug reactions. I was late on one particular day because of traffic and just missed an outburst from one of the veterans. He picked up a bench in the meeting room and threw it across the room just missing 10 people. Fortunately, no one was injured and the patient was taken safely to a quiet room. Nursing suddenly felt very real. I understood why many students make the decision to leave nursing. I did not.

Back to Nursing School

So, that is how my nursing school year started… with stress and fear. However, no such incidences returned. The semester quickly breezed by. I do remember experiencing compassion symptoms. There was not one psychiatric diagnosis I encountered, which I did not think I "owned". I started to think that I should have been in the hospital along with many of my patients. I simply could not believe the many diagnoses in Mental Health. And many patients had "dual diagnoses", which meant more Mental Health issues with multiple diagnoses. Thinking back, I remember having long discussions with many of my student pals about how organized and complex the human brain is. There were many debates over nature vs. nurture. My take has always been it is both and that all people are individuals. Many of us are more resilient than others, and it is difficult to predict who can or will become mentally ill or suffer chemical imbalances in the brain. Presently, because of the upgrades in medications, many patients can live a normal life and live at home and work under treatment. Still, there are many who will need extensive interventions with revolving door admissions.

Yes, nursing was finally starting to open up for me. I could finally experience the different avenues it offered. I liked psychiatric nursing but knew that I had to put that particular avenue on hold after graduation. I wanted to familiarize myself with all or most aspects of nursing before going into a specialty.

Ah finally, Christmas time with over three weeks off!!! YES, it was going to be a good Christmas as both parents were feeling well. Soon, I would be home again to my childhood place and bedroom. Our Christmas was wonderful. Getting together with childhood friends, relatives, and parties. I had made the decision to visit my sister Laurie and her husband Ramesh and nephew Andrew (2). It was a very exciting time for them as they were expecting a second child in May. California was fantastic and all it had to offer but ended very quickly. Soon, I was home in my student apartment and ready to start the more challenging medical-surgical clinical rotations.

Clinical Days

It was a very cold winter. I remember the difficulty I had getting out of bed at 4:30 am for a clinical day after preparing till 11:30 the night before. I had to be prepared for all the questions from my nursing instructors. It was not easy. I did continue to feel nauseous at times because of nerves. Some of the instructors were very kind, but there were some who were not. I thought I was in the military but knew that soon the day would be over. The pre conference was the most difficult. Being well prepared was expected. Preparedness included the complete patient's mental and medical history, along with their social history, medications, and all side effects of their medications. The day before, we had to introduce ourselves and share our expectations with each assigned patient.

The next morning, we had to share our knowledge with our peers and instructors along with being "drilled" by our instructors. As I stated, some were kind and others were not. There were times I felt I was back in grade school. I will say one thing, most of us were always prepared, and because of the strictness of this program, we learned a lot. Stress/fear is readily remembered along with joy and happiness. Are there nurses out there with PTSD (Post-Traumatic Stress Disorder), I wonder?

Our reactions to events depend on our stamina and resilience, which is individual. I did learn to develop "thick skin" and did overcome some of my sensitivity. That was one of the many gifts I received from nursing school. Many of these experiences were overwhelming. We had opportunities to observe surgeries in the operating room. I remember one particular St.

Patrick's Day, I was assigned labor and delivery and witnessed a woman giving birth to twins. This was a surprise because twins were not expected. I witnessed many scenes, some were very happy and others were not. I was with one man the day before exploratory bowel surgery. He shared with me his greatest fear would be to wake up in the recovery room with a colostomy (external bag on lower abdomen which collects feces). I remember going to visit him before he was fully conscious only to find out that yes, indeed a colostomy had to be created for him secondary to a life-threatening blockage. During this time and these rotations, I witnessed much--- diagnoses of cancer, infertility, heart attacks, seizures, and the list goes on and on. But I was learning. I was exposed to all of life's dramas, and I remember watching the effects of not only patients and their families, but the medical staff adjusting to the pain and suffering of others. I was in awe of their resilience and stamina – then to return the very next day and continue on.

The Emergency Room

Both during nursing school and throughout my working years, there are several stories that come to mind. I call them stories because they have a beginning and an end. One such "story" happened during my school rotation. I was assigned the Emergency Room (ER) during my medical rotation. All nursing students were assigned at different times, because of scheduling, I was one of the last to go. I was not worried or nervous because all who went ahead of me were having an easy time of it. I was hearing "don't worry", "piece of cake", etc. So, I arrived my first evening at around 4 pm and was expected to stay till around midnight to OBSERVE AND ASSIST as necessary. I was assigned two nurses to shadow and learn from. I started off a little tired and was hoping I would be able to stay awake as I was not used to these hours.

I was usually home studying and went to bed around 10:00 to prepare myself for the next day. No sooner was I in and introduced, when a very petite woman came through the ER doors unaccompanied. I happened to be right at the door as she came in. I was listening to her complaint when I glanced down at her left hand and found that the skin had been peeled off her entire hand and was hanging loosely off her wrist and attached by about 2 inches of skin. I was looking down at bone and cartilage only. I thought, OMG, now what. I quickly looked around and finally spotted a nurse close by. Fortunately, there was a wheel chair, and I quickly brought the patient to the emergency intake and bypassed the insurance intake area. Wow, did everyone act fast. I was actually able to assist in some way by obtaining a sterile bowl and pouring sterile saline in it for the patient to put her hand in. I was then instructed to take her vital signs. All this was done as they were lifting her on a gurney, ripping her clothes off, and putting in an IV. Then I knew and experienced what it was like to learn as most nursing students learn what do you do first. Well, there is almost always never a first. Many things get done simultaneously with many helping hands involved. Within 3-4 minutes, the patient was undressed, vital signs monitored, cardiac monitor on, oxygen placed and IV in. I was in charge of making sure the effected hand stayed intact and clean. I was then instructed to put sterile gloves on and wrap the effected hand in sterile gauze. Just as I finished, she no sooner was whisked up to the OR for surgery. And oops, during that time, the intake security went through her things and found a phone number to call, and her mother was enroute. The patient never lost consciousness, but I think she was in shock, which enabled her to stay conscious. I was talking to her throughout and found out what actually happened to her. She was a bus driver (large 40-seater), and one of the bus tires became flat. She had made the incorrect decision to attempt to change the tire herself, and as a result, somehow the bus landed on her hand as she was pulling her hand out from under the changed tire. I am not really sure how she got to the ER or what happened to the passengers on the bus, but she did arrive alone to the ER. Her family did arrive just as they were rolling her to the OR. I did hear later she did quite well and the hand was saved, but subsequent surgeries were needed.

A young man came in completely covered in blood from head to toe. The ER staff worked very quickly. As they were undressing him, I was instructed to locate where the injury was, which caused all the bleeding. Was it a gunshot or was it a stabbing? I felt like a failure because I could not find the injury. The patient was starting to lose consciousness because of blood loss. It was quickly determined that the blood loss was caused by a bleeding ulcer. This poor man had vomited up a lot of blood. My responsibility as a student nurse was to clean him up and put a clean johnny on him as they worked on him. Then again, it's not what you do first, many things get done simultaneously by many helping hands. He too, was sent to the OR in record time to tie off where the bleeding was. Well, finally, dinner at 8:00 pm and I was hungry. I took a 15-minute dinner break, and many did not have time to eat.

I was not prepared for this busy night. But the time was going by fast…I was thinking what next?? It was quiet for a couple of hours. Then bang, I was putting some supplies away when I heard a ruckus out in the main ER. Apparently, an older male patient came in with chest pain and was having a full-fledged heart attack. He did stop breathing and did not have a pulse. They worked on him for 10 minutes, and were able to bring him back. He was eventually transported up to the ICU and my responsibility was to ambu-bag him till he started to breath on his own, then assist in bringing him up to the unit. Everything happened so fast that night, I hardly remember what I was there for. I had no time to think of myself or my actions. It was now 11:30 pm, time to return home. I didn't feel right about leaving and felt I should have stayed longer, but I knew I couldn't. I said my goodbyes, and I was praised for my contributions. As I was driving home, I realized the importance of working as a team to ensure the best medical/psych/social care for each patient. The entire ER staff worked beyond their limits and never lost their professionalism.

That night was my last clinical rotation. I was to graduate within a week. My school had a beautiful candle-lit pinning ceremony for us, then the graduation ceremony where we received our diplomas. To have that diploma in my hand seemed like a miracle!!

Nursing Boards

Now that school was behind me and graduation parties over, this of course was a huge sense of relief. I had found a job and decided to work in a large teaching hospital in Boston. But it was not over, there were the nursing boards to pass. The panic started all over again.... studying, cramming (which I was never able to conquer)!! Thank God, my new job wasn't starting until August. What was I thinking, I would have the summer off and party, sail, and sleep. No way, my friend and close confidante Rose decided we would take a review course for two weeks plus study on the side. I was never a good test taker and always needed to study very hard to pass a test or at least to get and keep a B+ average. Rose and I had been through nursing school together, and we toiled and had many panic attacks together. We had a lot in common because of our age, second career, and were single without children. To this day, Rose is my friend and has been a wonderful support to me always.

The summer of 1981 was a very hot one and taking the train every day for two weeks into the city was tiring along with the stress of comprehending everything we had learned throughout nursing school and recramming it again over 14 days. Then there was the stress of the possibility of not passing the exam. The review course was a great help. It finished end of June, therefore giving me a long weekend off (4th of July) and returning to take the exam on July 6 for two days in Boston at an Army barrack located close to the Boston University campus. I had decided I had had enough of studying and figured if I did not know the information now, I would never know and threw caution to wind and went to Cape Cod to sail and party with my friends!! Which I did.

I returned and on the very next day took the train into Boston, which turned out to be one of the hottest days on record. To add insult to injury, I had the flu or a summer virus with a temp of 100°F. I felt dreadful with a sore throat and running nose. After registration, I sat with my quart of ice tea and 500 million Kleenex. This Kleenex was a huge problem as the test proctors had to closely watch me to ensure that I was not cheating. Each time I got up, they had to examine my Kleenex. After a while, they gave up and let me use the ladies room in peace without checking. Same same on day 2, still sick and with my temperature still about 100°F. All that I remember is going home and sleeping for two days. I did not have a sense if I had passed the exam or not, and that is what had scared me the most. I do remember being told not to discuss the test with any of your friends because if your answers were different, it would cause anxiety. We didn't listen, and we were all anxious!!

The rest of July flew by, and before I knew it, I was in my new job as a graduate nurse. We were all waiting for our test results. On my unit, there were 3 of us who were hired as new graduates. It was a busy medical-surgical unit, and we worked under an RN (orientation) until we received our board results. It was the end of August over a weekend when one of the nurses received a phone call from home. One of her roommates had received her result just that day and had passed. The three of us, Susan, Linda, and I had to work the whole day and worry. By the time I returned home, my hands were so shaky, I could not open the mail box. I recognized the envelope right on because my name was computerized, but off to the corner, I saw a number and knew that it was my registration # and that I had passed!! Yes, I was an RN! I called everyone there was to call. Mom #1 of course, then went out and spent money on a new watch with a second hand and an Etienne Aigner pocketbook!! I couldn't celebrate too much because I had to work the next day. However, the next day was not a happy one!! My two co-workers had not passed the exam and were quite upset about it. Of course, who wouldn't be! I felt bad and could not get too excited because it would have upset them. Our big plans for a party were cancelled on the unit. I did get a little shortchanged, but I celebrated outside work in a big way. Eventually, my co-workers retook the exam and did pass about 6-7 months later. The chances are very slim that out of 3 nurses on one unit that two did not pass. I felt hugely lucky and grateful that I had been on the upper side of this equation!!

New Nurse

The first unit I worked on was a very busy medical-surgical unit in a teaching hospital in Boston. What this means is having patients with medical conditions and patients going to have surgery were all on the unit. This, of course, is a wonderful opportunity to learn and receive a well-rounded education and great exposure for all nurses to learn and experience to a more advanced level. I felt grateful to have been selected and hired to work on this unit. Because of its diversity, we were all challenged.

Remembering one particular morning, every morning there would be medical rounds, which consisted of attending MD, medical students, surgical residents, head nurse, and the assigned nurse for the day. You would be lucky to be included in this because most of the time, most nurses were too busy running around. This particular morning, I could not attend rounds for this very reason. I was tending two ladies in a room across from a small unit, which housed four men. The medical round staff were just outside the doors in the hallway making both rooms easily visible. I glanced over to the "male room" to eyeball my patients (nurses do this continuously to check on the safety of their patients).

I noticed that one particular man "Mr. Brown" was sitting up in bed with his breakfast tray and appeared in distress. I immediately ran into the room bypassing the medical round staff, mind you, I had to practically run through them to save time, but nobody really noticed. By the time I got into the room, my patient "Mr. Brown" was choking and could not speak. I had no time but to act promptly by jumping on the bed and delivering the Heimlich

Maneuver. Several attempts were made, and within one minute, Mr. Brown was able to expectorate copious amounts of lime jello (patient was on a liquid diet). During this time, I thought it was strange that nobody even noticed or comprehended what was going on. The medical staff which was right outside the room at the doorway and looking in the same direction took no notice of a thing!!

They were so deep into receiving information and reporting information that they did not see a thing. I do realize that these rounds can be stressful most of the time with all the attendings, drilling the medical students, and sometimes not in such a nice manner. Finally, a 1st-year medical student saw me looking at him and realized what had just transpired and pointed into the room stating, "I think your nurse needs assistance." Of course, by that time, the patient was fine and breathing. Sometimes, you can go about your working day with your eyes wide shut!! Fortunately, all ended without a problem. To this day, I will not ingest lime jello!!

Cougar

I had been a nurse for about a year and was busy and into my nursing fulltime schedule. I barely had time for a social life in the early days but did find time to fit some socialization into my schedule. However, what I did, I should not have fit into my schedule. I was still working on the medical/surgical unit. Some of our cases were very critical and others were not.

This particular young man (25) was admitted for bunion surgery. He had been admitted the night before, and as I entered my early am shift the next day, they were transporting him onto the elevator as I was entering my unit. I remember feeling relieved that he had already been tended to earlier by the previous shift, allowing me to start my day a little ahead of schedule. He arrived promptly around 3-4 hours later in stable condition with all dressings intact and his foot on ice to prevent swelling. He was a great patient. I will call him "Kevin". He was on our unit for 5 days. Mind you, back in the early 80's, patients' length of stay was long compared to today in 2023, where for a bunionectomy, you would be expected to return home on the same day, provided there were no complications. I met his family, who happened to be well connected in the community (sorry, I will not give any more info), and I got to know Kevin who shared information with me about his career, hobbies, etc. Eventually, his discharge date was set. On the actual discharge day, I was his assigned nurse and did his entire discharge and reviewed his instructions and follow up appointments. He was discharged by the early afternoon.

I do remember thinking I wish all my patients could be so uncomplicated and kind. Later that same day, I had received a phone call. It was Kevin, and I was initially thinking, oh God, what did I forget? Well, I forgot nothing. He called to ask me for a date, and I had no time to think about it, and I immediately accepted. I couldn't believe what I was doing. Nurses really are not supposed to date patients. Anyway, he invited me over to his home that next Saturday evening to watch a movie with him. He could not drive because of his surgery and apologized, and of course, I understood. He gave me the directions to his home, which was in a very exclusive area of a South Shore coastal community. I arrived around 7 pm dressed casually. He had been staying with his parents till his healing was completed. As I drove up to their circular driveway to a doorway that was half the size of my apartment building, I was let in by a housekeeper. His parents were standing there stating, "We are on our way out to dinner, so you and Kevin can have the den to yourselves for the movie."

I felt very intimidated but decided to go along with the flow of things. This mansion probably had 20 rooms and was quite beautiful!! I was walked into the den where Kevin was sitting with his affected leg elevated. The parents left, and the movie started (do not even remember the movie but it was a big hit in 1982). We talked of many things and then my age was asked. I told him 31 because that was how old I was. It never occurred to me that he did not know my age, and I never looked my age. I have always looked younger than my years. He thought I was right out of nursing school, which I was. But for me, it was a second career which he did not know. He thought I was right out of nursing school aged 21-22 or 23 at the oldest. He was looking for someone younger not older. We were a little quiet for a while, and I have to say the evening pretty much went down the tubes!!

I tried to make the best of it, knowing I would not see him again, but "Kevin" didn't even try and had no manners or common sense or sensitivity as to what I was feeling. I waited for the movie to end and used the excuse that I had to drive back to Quincy, and it was raining. Yes, raining cats and dogs with a ton of fog and zero visibility along the coast. We said our goodbyes and out the door I went, never to hear from "Kevin" again. Many years later, his family continued to stay in the local news politically and had their hands in a few very big and successful businesses. Incidentally, I too live along the coast about 2 miles away from him. We do cross paths because of our close proximity!! I believe the disclosure of age is important, but a very important rule of thumb is – do not date patients. Lesson learned!

Take Care of Yourself

As a new nurse in a busy teaching hospital in Boston, MA, I was exposed to many opportunities for growth through learning, and working with a multicultural staff, but most of all, witnessing human behavior under duress, joy, sadness, and pain. Watching, seeing, and feeling my patients and their families review their lives and receiving horrific news brought a clear understanding of myself and my own frailties. I kept asking myself, how do they do it?

They seemed to have pulled up stamina and strength from deep within somewhere. I kept thinking, what if this was me and what would I do, and how would I feel? Now, I was starting to get it. I had always thought I was a compassionate person and was told that I had compassion. While in school, my focus was on studies and passing exams. For the first time, I could really feel what another is feeling and/or putting myself in their shoes. This affected me very deeply. Too deeply at times as I was starting to think about my patients on my days off and wondering how they were doing and making phone calls to other staff to check on them. Only then did I remember what was drilled into me while in school. Do not take work home with you, do things that make you happy, find hobbies, etc. Enjoy your life and live in joy. Fortunately, I became a better nurse for it, living a balanced life. I also learned the strength humans are capable of. So, no matter what happens to you, your strength is there to tap into.... just believe.

Addie and Dr. McDreamy

This is one of many very funny or sad stories or incidents I can remember. I had transferred to another unit at the same busy city teaching hospital. My original unit had closed due to restructuring. This new unit was a better match for me. The head nurse was kinder and allowed us to be autonomous. This new change allowed me to become a better and more relaxed nurse. "Ellen" seemed to understand her staff, further allowing the nurses to engage with their patients and to use the true primary care model for care. Such as, not only meeting the patients' physical needs but also psych-social and spiritual needs.

I started to learn and understand more of what nursing entailed. I finally could understand for myself and have the ability to experience nursing on a broader perspective. Treating the whole human and giving patients what they needed. Sometimes, it was just leaving them alone to their own thoughts and feelings and other times to spend additional time with them with their permission. One particular woman, I will call her "Addie," had joined us after surgery. She was quite ill for a while after undergoing vascular surgery to her lower extremities. Many times, the anesthesia is hard to clear, and Addie was temporarily confused for about a week. Every morning, she would cry out "I want to die, I want to die," the doctors and surgeons worked with her daily, not to mention the nursing staff. We did not want to complicate her condition by giving her sedatives. She had round-the-clock care, and she repeated herself round the clock, "I want to die, I want to die." Poor Addie did not say anything, but the same thing over and over except for an occasional yes or no.

Day in and day out, we were all so worried for her, wondering when she would be clearing or burning off this anesthesia. She was carefully monitored daily, and I knew she was receiving the best possible care. One particular am, a new surgical resident was sent in to review "Addie" for his first time. We had explained to him the situation, so off he went in to meet Addie with chart in hand. As he opened the door, he was serenaded with "I want to die, I want to die." Then there was silence for about a minute or so. As the resident was leaving Addie's room, he was further serenaded with "I want to live, I want to live, and hey, you come back here." I am sure it had something to do with his great looks and stature. We all fell in love with Dr. McDreamy that rotation. Fortunately, Addie did start to clear and was less confused as time went on. To this day, I wonder if the appearance of Dr. McDreamy and his great looks were responsible for Addie's change in status.

Letting Go

As I said previously, many or most of my memories are extremely comical stories. But there are a few that are very sad. Back in the early 80's, HIV/Aids was just being discovered, although it had been around for a while, but the major teaching hospitals were starting to discover that many of the patients, especially young male patients, were arriving by the droves in ER's with very similar symptoms and unfortunately dying within an 6-18-month time frame. Of course, HIV effects everyone, but in the early days, it was inaccurately labeled a "gay disease". The hospital I was working in was admitting many of these unfortunate young men by the dozens. Our hospital had a very large and successful infectious disease department, hence, all the admissions.

One particular young man "John" was admitted and put into a private room. All admissions with diagnosis of unknown etiology were put in private rooms and subjected to precaution signs outside their room along with medical carts supplying all staff entering the room with precaution gowns, gloves and masks. This was done for their protection as well as ours. This prevented medical staff from passing germs on to compromised patients and also protected all staff from acquiring "unknown viruses." Well, John was only about 22 years old and had met most or all of the criteria for a diagnosis of HIV with active AIDS. He was not doing well, his lungs were failing, along with cancer, and other maladies of AIDS. He was well aware of his diagnosis and was receiving care from most of our departments. His friends would visit him. But as the days went by, he was getting weaker and weaker, and medically there was not much for us to do for him except to keep him comfortable. I was John's primary nurse and pretty much saw him every day I worked. Some days, I could talk to him for an extended period of time, and other days I was caught up with just having enough time to care for him because of many other patients with emergencies.

This particular day, my schedule was light (miracle), and I chose to spend time with John. We talked of many things, and I had noticed that I never saw any family members around. He explained to me that his family did not agree with his homosexual lifestyle and had disowned him about two years previously. He had written and called to inform them of his diagnosis and of his life-ending disease. He was waiting to hear from them. The social worker got involved and put a call into his family in Connecticut. But there was never a response. John was failing quickly. I did not know what to do for him. I started to think about it and decided to "take the bull by the horns." It was a quiet Sunday, and I was working 7-3. Around lunchtime, I donned my precaution gown and decided to sit with him for a while. I do not remember my exact words, but in so many words, I asked him if he was afraid to die. He said upfront and to the point. "No, I'm not, just waiting to see my mom." Daily, he would inquire if his mother had called and if there was any mail. I knew that his mom wasn't coming because she had told the social worker that she would not be coming or calling. John did not know this but everybody else did and decided not to tell him, and I was not going to tell him either. But I thought I could do something for him knowing this information.

I decided to tell him that it was alright to let go of life at any time he was ready. I sat with him for a while in silence. And said again that it was his decision when he was ready. He looked at me, and I knew he was ready. About

45 minutes later, I went in and found that John was in the throws of actively dying. He of course was a DNR (Do-Not-Resuscitate). I was with John for his last breath. When I think back to that episode, I feel very grateful that John was my teacher, giving me the opportunity to assist him through this transition. He had a very peaceful and fast death. We did his post mortem care in silence. I discovered that sometimes patients need permission to let go, and that as difficult as it is for a close family member or friend to do, the effected person is waiting for that very special "green light" to the afterlife.

Ballet

As a new nurse, we all had to rotate to different shifts. I preferred days/evenings and despised nights; however, I did not have a choice. It was not my first night, but this particular night came later. It was a rare quiet night on a busy medical/surgical floor. One of the many responsibilities of a night shift nurse was to get the patients ready for the OR, the next morning if they were scheduled. All charts had to have labs, chest x-rays, anesthesia authorization, and surgeon's signature, patient teaching, all pre-op preps must be completed and rested on the shoulders of the night shift to ensure that all was done and documented in the chart, and the patient was ready and that he/she knew why they were going to the OR.

As I said, this night was a quiet one and only 1-2 were scheduled for the morning. We had time on our hands. Now, let me tell you when you get a group of nurses together, we all like a few laughs. We took our nursing seriously, but this particular group I was with liked to have some "fun" on occasion. I will add, never at the expense of a patient. We got to talking, and we had one thing in common. All of us had loved ballet. There was a ramp on our unit, and we decided to put it to use. We all practiced our running leaps, twirls, and pilates. This went on between patient checks 1:30-2:30 am, and oh, what great fun we had!! The night continued on and stayed quiet. Soon, our shift was over, and the two OR charts were completed. The patients were scheduled for 9 am ORs, so they were still in their room by the time we signed off and went home to sleep. I was scheduled to work the next night (my last one for a while).

I came on my usual time 10:45 pm for report and narcotic count. During receiving report, I noticed one of the patients (Mr. Smith) had not gone to his scheduled surgery and I asked why? It was reported to me that his surgeon had checked on him in the morning before surgery (a normal occurrence) and found the patient to be confused; surgery was temporarily cancelled and the patient had a psych. evaluation pending with a review of his labs. I, of course, asked why?? The answer I received was that the surgeon had found his patient confused and again I asked, confused about what? He was fine the night before. According to the note written in the chart, OR cancelled secondary to patient confusion. The patient stated he witnessed, "ballerinas dancing in the hallway last night," I could not believe it. I quickly reported to one of the other night nurses as the other two were off. What are we to do!! We have to tell the surgeon. The only thing we could do was to beep the surgical resident in the hospital, but the surgeon was home in bed. So, we came clean and explained that the patient was not confused and that we had been dancing. Eventually, the head surgeon did find out but was not mad but relieved. The patient did eventually go to surgery within 72 hours. Well, we never did that again!!

Bar Fight

I had been nursing now for over a couple of years on the same unit and feeling a little more relaxed and more sure of myself. But, at the same time, you never knew what was coming your way. I always said to expect the unexpected and that little cliché ran true. On this particular evening, I believe it was late winter early springtime. I had been taking care of this man for over two weeks. He had suffered complications after gallbladder surgery but was well on his way to recovery. As a result, I became pretty familiar with his family (big mistake) especially his unmarried son who was very nice, kind, and patient. He ended up asking me out for a drink or coffee, and I accepted (big mistake no#2).

I was working the evening shift and planned to meet him in a fairly decent piano bar up the street from where I lived. We met, talked, I ordered wine, and I think he had a beer. All was well for about 30 minutes. Unfortunately, there was a very drunk man sitting beside me at the bar who started to mouth off. Of course, initially, we ignored him (date's name was Peter), then we decided to change our seating and move to a table which had become vacant. As we were transferring, several comments were made about us in a very derogatory manner. Peter, of course, must have felt as though he was put on the spot and had to speak up.

I felt so bad because neither of us expected this to happen. I do not remember exactly what was said, but I am sure Peter asked him to stop. At this point, everything happened so fast, before I knew it, fists were flying, and two bodies were rolling on the floor. The fight was quickly broken up, and all of us were escorted out the door. The drunk man was taken to the police station, and fortunately, no one was injured. I said I was sorry and was in shock, and I am sure Peter was as well. We said our goodbyes in the parking lot, and I drove on home. I never saw Peter again. I was scheduled off of work for two days, and when I returned, Peter's father had been discharged home. I was very relieved in more than one way. I admit that it was a mistake on my part, but I realize it was just bad luck. To this day, I do occasionally have to drive by that same piano bar and will always remember that night.

Bats

And… another story comes to mind. I was helping out on the night shift 11-7 am. It was a typically busy night making sure all the charts were in order for the patients having surgery the next day, along with taking care of the patients, who were fresh out of the operating room, and of course, handling emergencies. There were always emergencies as we were an acute care unit. We had lots of IVs, chest tubes, (punctures in the lung to help patients breathe and to keep the lung expanded), feeding tubes, and tubes going down into and through the esophagus and stomach to either feed patients or to keep their stomachs empty by bringing up secretions through suction. The list goes on and on, but our biggest challenge was to keep a patient comfortable with medications to ensure comfort and safety.

Now, I mention safety because it is the most important of all nursing care. We have to keep ourselves safe, other staff and of course patients. This night was no different. Our unit had a huge laundry chute, which had a door that opened into an even bigger chute. We had many wonderful NA's (nursing assistants), which one of their many responsibilities was to change the linens when needed. At about 12:30 in the morning, I looked down into our unit and noticed two NA's running towards me with their coats over their heads totally obliterating their faces and heads. I could only think at the time, now what!! What could possibly be going on now. Of course, I had to ask "why do you have your coats draped over you like that?" My answer was "Kitty, there is something in the laundry shaft that is alive." "What?" I responded in not such a patient tone. So, off I went in the direction of the laundry chute, and as I opened the door, all I could hear was a fluttering of something with wings. I quickly slammed the door almost knocking it off its hinges. Another nurse braver than myself reopened the door and out flew something – well, maybe more than one. Only we could not identify it, it really did not look like a bird. By this time, I was on the phone calling the night supervisor and housekeeping. The return telephone call confirmed our worse fears…that there had been a previous complaint from the unit below us. "UFO's unidentified flying objects!

They were eventually identified as BATS!! Yes, BATS!! I had only seen bats in magazines and/or on TV but, had never seen them with the naked eye. We never knew how they got there. But it was explained to us from housekeeping that they found their way into the vent system. Well, I honestly did not care how they got there, I just wanted them out and right away!! Housekeeping managed to return them back into the vent system, then outside. All was well, and order was restored once again. But I will always remember my true encounter with UFO's (small black kind) on my hospital unit. My nursing career was more involved than I had hoped or wanted it to be.

Holistic

As my career progressed, I had to make a decision to enter graduate school and focus on becoming an NP or furthering my managements skills and entering management permanently. Since I could not decide, I rejected both options. I was leaning into holistic health and became very interested in the spiritual side of life and questioning life, past lives? And my soul's journey. I knew it would always be assisting others with their health, but I always felt that all healing took place on much deeper levels. We are all separate from each other but at the same time very connected to each other and to earth. I was feeling this on a much deeper level and felt the feeling of being intertwined.

Now, back to 1986. I was working in a SICU (Surgical ICU). I had just completed my training and loved the unit I was to be part of. Third month on the job, I went skiing and suffered a severe left knee injury (completely tearing all of my ligaments). This put me out of work for almost three years.

Initially, I became interested in the spiritual world when I was in my mid-twenties and had read many books, such as Kubler-Ross, The Souls Journey, Lobsang Rampa, and many many more. I couldn't read them fast enough. And I did share a lot of what I read and did always receive mixed reviews, but many more people started to become interested as well and more books were being published on the spiritual realm. The issues addressed were life after death, past lives, alternate methods of healing, microbiotic food, and changes in dealing with mental health illness. I think my awareness with some of these fragments of "healing" made me became more aware of my patients. I was able to view my patients on a deeper and more complex level. I saw disease as a process of imbalance. This imbalance was present because of many other issues present within the mind, body, and psyche.

I was to learn that we could actually carry these illnesses with us from past lives and unresolved problems from past lives. After researching much, I decided to put some of these modalities into use and experience some of these processes and treatments myself. I happened to meet a very spiritual and gifted healer (name withheld upon request). She explained to me that all living creatures have an energy field around them with colors called an aura. Through reading this aura, you can see a person's life path of past, present, and future – as well as disease and potential disease. There are very few gifted healers who can see this and interpret it accurately. I was very fortunate enough to meet this special lady and work with her. I do not possess this insight, but there have been times my strange intuition has assisted me and my patients.

I studied all levels of Reiki and received my Masters Certificate. I found all levels useful in healing, and when used in conjunction with Western Medicine.

Rice Krispies

Another memory which comes to mind happened while I was finishing my rehab after suffering from the ski injury. I was on medical disability and slowly getting back into nursing but not full time. I took advantage of my time off and returned to school to get my Bachelor of Science degree. I worked per diem 1-2 shifts per week, which is what my MD allowed. I signed up to an "agency" and was sent to many different places. One particular place was a favorite of mine. It was a rest home for the financially challenged. It was a melting pot of aged homeless, aged ex-inmates, and adults with cognitive and mental disabilities. My favorite lady was Miriam, a 55-year-old with Downs Syndrome who had been placed right after birth in an orphanage and became a child of the state at one week old. I had agreed to work a Saturday shift 7-3. I arrived early to receive report, do narcotic count, and rounds before the previous 11-7 nurse left for the day.

As soon as I walked in, I felt a "vibe" that things were not as they should be. Miriam was waiting for me at the door to tell me something. She looked very concerned and worried, stating, "We have no breakfast." Slowly, I ascended the stairs from the back parking lot door, thinking, "What have I gotten myself into today." I wanted to run back down the stairs and get into my car and drive off but knew that I could or would never do that. Sure enough, as per report from the 11-7 nurse, the cook would not be in this morning and that nobody had had their breakfast. I asked, trying to maintain my cool. "Well, what do you usually do in a situation like this?" The answer I received was, "This has never happened before, and I don't know, call the administrator on call" (OMG, I should have gone home!!). Keep in mind that this facility is very small with 40 patients and one nurse with about 4-5 nursing assistants. When the RN comes on duty, you are the nurse in charge of the whole facility when you arrive and that includes the housekeeping staff!! Fortunately, the keys I received for my shift had the key to the administration office. I called right away and fortunately a lady answered who was the head administrator. I quickly updated "Mrs. Smith" on the situation and the instructions I received were to open her drawer, look for a box, then open the box where there was a small amount of cash. But before I could do that, I had to open the kitchen and dining area to see what food supplies we had. I was pretty much told to arrange for the NA staff to prepare breakfast. However, nobody could use the big stove or knew how it worked!!

I was instructed to call Mrs. Smith back after figuring out what to do. There was orange juice, coffee, eggs, bacon, oatmeal, and milk, but no cereal. So, I decided it would be a cold breakfast only. I sent one of the NA's out to the store to buy cereal – any cereal – and the menu would be cereal, milk, juice, and coffee. That would have to suffice till the lunchtime cook arrived!! Joseph (NA) had returned with cereal, stating "All they had were Rice Krispies." I said fine now, let's get these patients fed. I was starting to get concerned for the diabetics. All the patients were quickly ushered into the dining area and fed an adequate breakfast. I remember checking the dining area about 30 minutes later. I walked into a room of silence and crunching of Rice Krispies popping. Forty bowls of popping rice crispies!! What a sound! I decided to let everyone eat their late breakfast in peace. As I was walking down the hallway outside of the dining area, I could still hear the popping of Rice Krispies.

To this day, whenever I see a Rice Krispies box, I remember that Saturday morning back in the winter of 1987. And of course, times have changed! I can't imagine there would be an available key to a cash box, but thank God it was there on that cold winter morning. I do remember the lunch cook did arrive and was I ever grateful to see him!

Frank

I had the wonderful opportunity and became a hospice nurse for two years. You're asking why only two years…some nurses come on board and last 2-6 months, others stay a lifetime. It was a huge challenge, and I worked with very dedicated professionals. I had made the decision to move on after two years because variety was my original goal, but mostly, the politics got in the way. We were a smaller facility, and many of us (always the nurses) had to wear several hats, meaning take on many other duties outside of our job descriptions. This I did not mind working a little extra, but as time went on, I found it tiring and started to burn out. But I must share a few experiences with you. I knew that death and dying is serious business and at all times all patients and their families were treated with respect and compassion.

I will apologize now if I offend anyone. Just remember, people are human, and that being said, humor will always find its way into any or most situations. It was summer time, and most of my hospice district consisted of the area in and surrounding the city of Boston. It was my last visit for the day (I thought), and it appeared that Mrs. Smith was settled and comfortable. As I was leaving, my Beeper went off. Back then, we had beepers and large cell phones. The protocol was to call the office and the administration assistant would give you the message. Cheryl sounded a little nervous and requested to please call the Noel family immediately. My patient's (Frank) wife answered the phone (Mary), requesting that Frank had not eaten all day and to please come over to check him out. He was on my list to see first thing in the morning, but, of course, I went over and was there by 5:00 pm. Frank and

Mary lived directly in the city and not in the best of neighborhoods, which is why my visits were always in the morning. As I walked in, I found Mary in the kitchen preparing dinner for herself and Frank. I went directly to Frank who was residing in a hospital bed in their living room.

Frank had been very ill for a long time and had the diagnosis of end stage pancreatic cancer. I immediately saw that something was wrong. He did not respond to me when I gently shook him nor did he answer me back. I quickly checked his pulse, but there was none. Frank had expired (died). Unfortunately, Mary had not realized this and fed him his breakfast at 6 am, then again lunch was given to him at 12:00 noon… and he was well on his way to receiving dinner. Mary stated, "He's not swallowing his food and is keeping it in his mouth." Well, that was what he was doing…his entire oral cavity and cheek areas were stuffed with unswallowed food. Poor Frank looked like a chipmunk.

I knew I had to clean him up and cover him up, but before I did, I had the very sad task of telling Mary that Frank had died. He had been dead for over 10 hours, but I did not tell her that. She did not understand at first but then she did understand. I called her daughter out of state who went on to call the other relatives. After doing the post mortem care and all necessary paperwork, I went to call the chosen funeral parlor. Well again....it had not been done. Remember when I said earlier that the nurses had to wear many caps, and this was one of those times. The social worker had not made arrangements with the family. I quickly called the office and spoke to the director of social work and was told to use the YELLOW PAGES and find someone willing to come to a very dangerous neighborhood to a family who had no monetary reserves. I did what I was told and did eventually find a group of human angels willing to come out and remove Frank's remains.

This was a very special funeral parlor who was not only willing to come out immediately but had a sliding scale for poorer families and did not expect any money if at all until after the funeral or wake, which is what the family wanted. Frank did not want to be cremated. However, this took several phone calls with family members agreeing and/or disagreeing. I called Texas, Rhode Island, Missouri, and Massachusetts. This was not settled until close to 9 pm. Eventually, all was done, and I stayed with Mary until Frank was removed, which I didn't mind. Now, there was the problem of walking through the indoor dangerous garage. I felt the funeral company had sensed this, and I was escorted to my automobile. The next day was our weekly IDT meeting, and I will tell you I was not a happy camper and I let it be known.

Fast Trip Down

Another unusual remembrance comes to mind during my 2 hospice years. Remember, I worked close to and in the city. This particular city neighborhood was on a busy street, and the homes were close together (colonials). They had been built on a very steep ledge back in the 1940's. I remember climbing at least 20 stairs to get to the house. As I entered the house, I had an additional 13 steps to climb to visit the patient in his upstairs bedroom. Now, I want to take a moment to describe the outlay of the house. It was a colonial – after climbing 20 odd steps to get to the house, directly in front of you, there was a small area to rest before climbing additional 5-6 stairs which entered into the house. Then after opening the front door, there was a small foyer which led directly to 13 additional steps to the upstairs bedrooms. Of course, my patient (John) was upstairs. Well, I certainly received my cardiac workout making visits to this house. I remember during my first visit looking down from the top floor directly onto the sidewalk outside straight down 38 stairs!! WOW, I enjoyed visiting John and his family. They always had a treat waiting for me as I arrived. I usually never expected or accepted little treats, but I could not say "no" to this family.

Eventually, the inevitable happened. John was declining rapidly, and my visits increased. I remember it was a Monday morning, I received the call that John had just passed. His family was exceptional with his care as well as the Nursing Assistants.

He was my first stop for the day. I had all my paper work ready. Of course, the family was very quiet, saddened, and crying. I gave my condolences and quickly went upstairs to do the "death pronouncement." As I was finishing, I glanced out the window and was glad that the funeral home company had arrived to pick John up to continue onto his journey. It was quite cumbersome for the handlers to carry the heavy gurney all the way up those stairs. I wondered how they would manage, not only the steps but the steep incline. As I was finishing the paperwork, John had been strapped onto the gurney and covered in a plastic shroud. As they were leaving, I heard a big thump. The handlers had dropped the gurney and down the stairs went John, safely strapped in on wheels… then again directly outside to the front 5 stairs and down he went with no assistance, and to my horror and that of the funeral home handlers, down the last 20 icy slippery stairs and landed directly in front of the hearse.

Fortunately, this was only witnessed by myself and the handlers. The family had moved into the kitchen as they did not want to see John actually leave his house. We were all shell-shocked. One family member did make it into the living room and said, "Boy, they really move fast." I decided at that point that I would not share with anyone what I had just witnessed. All was well, John remained intact and strapped in with no damage to anyone or anything. I did not report anything because I thought that there was nothing to report. If I had, I think that poor funeral handler would have lost his job. Sometimes, it is better to just stay quiet.

Gifts

One of the many benefits of caring for others is receiving "gifts." Although it has been embedded into our heads during nursing school, "never to accept any form of a gift." I have to say that this is very difficult and sometimes, you have to just say yes, which of course I readily did. I never accepted money although I was offered. Before I was a nurse, I worked 4 years as a Medical Assistant both in a doctor's office and in a hospital. The generosity of patients overwhelmed me at times. I have to remember, how grateful patients become when they receive care, compassion, and kindness. Not only the inpatient hospital but also in the outpatient setting!

Many of the patients eventually become like family members. One particularly kind but very sick lady "Janice" was receiving chemotherapy in the office I worked in for breast cancer. I would check her vital signs and was also responsible for checking her blood levels to determine her dose of chemotherapy. Janice heard through the grapevine that I was planning a long trip to Europe for a month and must have heard me complain of my lack of appropriate attire and limited funds. Her husband owned a clothing factory in the manufacturing district. She invited me to the factory on a Saturday to pick out clothes. I did not accept and thanked her profusely. The following week, she brought me several jerseys and sweaters just my size. Well, what was I to say!

Another kind man (Frank) with a very unusual type of anemia (polycythemia) instead of too little blood, he had too much. One of my jobs was to actually remove blood from him. Now, before you label me as Dracula or Werewolf, instead of drawing 1-2 tubes of blood for testing which I frequently did, I removed up to 12 tubes under the direction of the MD. This improved his breathing and prolonged his life to prevent blood clotting. He always felt better after. Frank was an overseas travelling salesman and would visit many exotic places. One morning, I came to work and found a beautifully wrapped package with my name on it. Inside was a beautiful blue cloth evening purse with gold leaflet needled patterns. I still use it to this day for very special occasions.

Another gift I remember was from one of my first patients. His name was "Morey" and stood 6 feet six inches. We always made a spectacle of ourselves ambulating up and down the hallways because I was barely 5 feet tall!! He was on my unit for a very long time because of diabetic complications. He was a restaurant owner and knew many in the business. His parting gift to me was to visit a favorite and popular Chinese restaurant any time I wanted free of charge. I did visit twice with a friend.

Lois who was dying of leukemia and eventually did pass on, but she was able to make it home one last time gifted me with a beautiful set of pearls, which to this day I wear and will always think of her. I was also lucky to have several patients who were and probably still are artists. "Bernice" made beautiful figurines inside egg shells. On her day of discharge, I was presented with a beautiful egg with the figure of a nurse inside. This sits in my kitchen cabinet.

Another artist "Bob" sent me a beautiful print of one of his floral scenes, which is now in a guest bedroom. I worked two years as a hospice nurse and made home visits. One elderly lady "Esther" was at the end of her life and very comfortable with letting go (one of my easier cases). She had passed the weekend I was off. I went to the nursing home on Monday to take care of paperwork. I was directed to go into her room. I did not know why because I knew she was not there, and it saddened me. But I did go, then I figured out why ...on her wall was a picture (antique) I always commented on it when I would visit her. My name was on it. I explained to the head nurse that I thought it should go to the family. I received a response. "Kitty, they wanted you to have it, it was left for you." I thought I was going to cry and did end up crying when I reached my car. Of course, I don't want to leave out the Chinese terranium, homemade apron, delicious goodies and food, and kind and heartfelt cards. It overwhelms me – the kindness and generosity I received during my tenure as a caregiver.

Onions and Tomatoes

I worked as a nurse liaison for a short while. This was a short while because I was hired and no sooner, I received word that the rehab would be closing, and another company would be "buying us out." However, the job did last a year. My job description entailed going to many different hospitals and reviewing charts to assess for the need for acute rehab. Rehabilitation falls under many categories.... cardiac, pulmonary, orthopedic, neuro-psych and psych. This hospital was very unique as they had a program for the morbidly obese. It had a huge success rate.

On this particular day, I was sent to a nursing home to assess a woman with an eating disorder. Usually, you never really know what you are going to step into, and this day was no different. After parking my car and finding the front door, I noticed the bushes to my right to be rustling. I was initially frightened because this area was having a recent coyote problem. As I further investigated, I found, no, this is no animal – this is a human being. A middle-aged woman was crouched down behind the bush. As I looked, she stood up and looked at me with a look of fear. I decided to report my findings as soon as I got inside, as I did not want to become engaged and have her run away.

I quickly found out that the patient I was to assess was missing and that the police had been called. I gave my report quickly and security was sent outside to "collect her." I did review her chart only to find that she had not been taking her psychological medications, and because of this, her diagnosis of schizophrenia/psychosis had exacerbated. She believed she could only survive on tomatoes and onions and had only eaten tomatoes and onions for

5 days straight. Just that morning, they had explained to her that she would be transferred out temporarily to another facility to help her get better. And of course, this is not what she wanted hence her disappearing act!! Just my fortunate luck, I was the one to find her. Mrs. Smith (fictitious) was seriously ill with a huge weight loss along with starvation. Time was of essence. She would not sign herself out and was considered incompetent. Therefore, the courts had to step in and sign her papers.

Fortunately, this process took all of 20 minutes, and she was out the door via ambulance in a four-point restraint. I did learn several weeks later that she did receive the help she needed with a medication adjustment and counselling. Mrs. Smith eventually did end back to her original facility. There is an addendum to this story.... There was a glitch, and it did take longer than I thought for the insurance company to give the ok for reimbursement.

I had many conversations with Mass Health via the phone over the care needed to sustain life for my patients. They would not budge. Without protein and proper diet and medication/counseling, death was imminent. Fortunately, the rehab I worked for accepted her anyway and helped continue the fight after the patient's admission. Most or all facilities do not accept patients without prior authorization or payment. Eventually, Mass Health granted acceptance with payment and it all worked out. Without proper care, this patient would have died of secondary starvation.

Escape

I know I have mentioned this before, but one of the many privileges and benefits of nursing are the many opportunities to move around and experience many differ locales, different specialties, and meet and befriend various and interesting people. This includes the indigent homeless population. I had experience in med-surg, critical care, dialysis, and transcultural nursing with management / Leadership skills. Now, my next step! I will admit I did not know what my next step would be, but it did come to me after my return from Saudi Arabia. I was blessed with this opportunity and met very many gifted and dedicated care givers (Drs, NPs, PAs, NAs, RNs, SWs, etc.). I have never seen or experienced people work so hard as a team and succeed!! I started off as a staff nurse and worked my way up to Nurse Manager. And of course, we had our very challenging times with much of the homeless population. It was very sad at times to have patients reappear again and again, even after placement with jobs, only to have them lose their employment and return again to the streets. It was a difficult job and many of the staff can continue on for several years, but some last only a couple of weeks. My tenure was three years. The experiences during this time were plentiful and enrichening. And also, funny and sad!!

One particular memory comes to mind. The unit I worked in was a medical respite for the homeless. It was a short-stay medical infirmary. When the homeless would come to us, we would work as a team and deal with substance abuse, jobs placement, and of course, the medical issue which brought them to us in the first place. It was difficult to meet the older homeless. Many times, they would "AWOL" on us, only to return a few weeks later, beat up and social security check (welfare) stolen. This one particular man "Shawn" had been homeless for years and lived at one of the neighboring shelters during the night hours. We worked very hard this time to get him placed through Medicaid to a rest home, where he would be safe and warm with 3 meals a day and able to receive his cardiac meds. It took the work of Jobe to accomplish this. The doctor, social workers, and nurses worked very hard to get it all together... which they did. The hardest part of this job was convincing "Shawn". He eventually agreed and signed himself into the rest home.

The big day was finally here, and I remember it well. It was a Friday before a long weekend. I specifically arrived to work early at 6:30 am. I had to drive up a hilly area. As I turned up the street, I was met with "Shawn" walking rather quickly down the street on the side walk and about 50 yards behind him was his case manager chasing him and behind her was his medical provider Jim looking quite angry and red in the face. I pulled over, but it was too late. "Shawn" escaped into the woods and off he went. He knew where he was going and had us all tricked!! All that hard work however, it was not for nothing. The seeds had been planted, and "Shawn" did eventually go into the rest home. It took us about one year to finally get him in to stay for good. I think he finally realized that life on the streets was getting too rough for him, and his fighting days were over for good. There were many more very similar situations as this one. The homeless staff are one of the most dedicated group of people I have known. But what a memory that was witnessing "Shawn" almost running down the street with his cane, then the social worker after him, then the MD after the social worker!!

Dave

I was still at the medical respite for the homeless when I met "Dave" during one of the hottest summers known to mankind. Some of the areas had AC, but the holding area or patient area had fans until the AC was installed. It was a weekend, I think a Sunday evening, and the heat spell was atrocious. All the units were cranked up with fans, then suddenly, we had a grey-out and lost most of our power. That's when I first met Dave who was a fairly new admission with a diagnosis of uncontrolled diabetes. He came to us for blood sugar monitoring and insulin control.

Dave looked as though he did not belong to us. He was tall, very athletic looking, and dressed the part. I thought he was a volunteer for sports and looked as though he had just run off the Harvard football field. His story was a sad one. Looks are deceiving. He had lost his job, his girlfriend had been murdered, and because of either drug or alcohol issues, his diabetes was out of control, and he was homeless. Meanwhile, on this very hot Sunday evening, we were all running around and trying to figure out what to do before it got dark!!

We had to gather up the patients, check on safety, make sure they had their dinner, find flashlights, check on our own safety, and distribute medications, etc., the list went on and on. "Dave" stepped right up to the plate and herded all the patients to one area and did continuous building checks (3 floors). Without him, I do not know what I would have done. It was like an angel appeared out of nowhere to help us out. Weekends and holidays are different than weekdays, as there is a skeleton crew and only 1-2 security staff, which were busy locating the plant engineer!! However, we did survive, but it took several hours to sort everything out. But I felt I wanted to mention "Dave" because he was such a hero to all of us that evening. I must admit I was feeling a little scared as I did not know if there were any violent patients among us, and I also did not know if the electronic panel had been tampered with. But thankfully, that was not the case.

Dave stayed with us well into the fall as it took a while to control his diabetes. He was eventually placed west of Boston in a male halfway house with employment and the opportunity to start school. I want to publicly thank Dave for all he did. And by the way, Dave is his real name. If you are reading this, thank you again for helping us out on that very hot Sunday evening!!

Safety – Working in a Prison

During my ten-year tenure as being a "prison nurse," I have to say there was only one time I did not feel safe. During my prison career, almost everyone would ask me: How can you work there? Aren't you scared? Has anyone ever threatened you? But mostly why? I will tell you why. My goal was when I chose the nursing profession, I wanted variety and to experience people in different surroundings and grasp life and its adversities through people. I wanted to be their eyes but not their diseases. I started off as a med-surgical nurse in a large teaching hospital, then I moved on to the ICU for a very short time. I had gone skiing and underwent extensive left leg surgery and was out of work for close to three years. During this time, I took advantage of the time and returned to school and earned my bachelor's degree. Finally, when I was ready to return, it was discovered I could not completely maneuver around in an ICU, so I chose Hemodialysis in an acute setting which I loved. After two years, I decided to move abroad and work in a foreign country. I worked in Saudi Arabia in a hospital servicing the Middle East in ophthalmic surgery. I was able to assist in starting up teaching programs for diabetes and earned a chance to enter management. I will tell you more about Saudi Arabia later.

After three years, I returned home and worked with the homeless population as a nurse and nurse manager, then onto Hospice for two years and then worked as a nurse liaison for a rehab until they closed shop. I took an 8-month break (overdue) and had a chance to breathe and smell the roses. What next? I have to say that corrections found me, and I do not know how or why that happened. Someone had called my mother and gave her their name with instructions for me to call them. I found this strange as I was not living at home with my mother. I happened to drop in to visit her one day and found the message. I did follow up, and the rest is history. I was onto a 10-year experience with corrections. People ask why? I respond why not!! So, off I went.

It took quite a while before I finally went to work. After 80 plus hours of training, blood tests, finger printing, and background checks, I was finally given a start date of Nov 1999. This process started in late August. I was one of ten nurses to start in the training, and by the time we all started to actually work, I and one other nurse were left. All others had left. But I did not have a problem with that. Sometimes, it takes a stronger person to leave, knowing that they made a wrong decision than to stay and feel miserable. However, I was glad that I stayed (10 years)!!

Now, I know that I did digress a little here and wanted to explain a little about my history and my decisions. I initially did think a lot at the beginning of the safety issues but had decided that if other nurses could stay, then why couldn't I. I did work in one prison mostly, but I did help out a lot at different facilities. I did like to help out at the bootcamp and found it very interesting. It was set up as a military-like bootcamp to scare the 18-25-year-olds straight. Sorry I cannot go into too much detail, but those young men were so scared. I hope it did work, but because of budget cuts, they had to close the place. I ended up helping out in about 4-5 other facilities as well as my home base job. One particular prison was very old, and I heard haunted as well. The stories would fly, and I guess the spirits did, too (I never did see anything).

We had a code 99 one night (medical emergency), and the officers would always accompany you where you had to go plus carry the emergency equipment. It was a very cold winter night, and I remember crossing the alley to another antiquated building. The emergency was in a barracks like room which housed about 50 beds and inmates in bunks. Well, I was initially relieved because the "patient" was sitting up in bed and talking. I was thinking, well this is no big emergency!! I soon felt very uncomfortable, realizing that there were about 50 of them and about 8 of us. My intuition was telling me to get out fast. People were just standing around lingering a little too long.

I had remembered stories of setups and diversion, and I was hoping this was not the case. I was feeling quite anxious and demanded that we move the patient to the HSU (Health Service Unit) for further medical evaluation because he was healthy enough to move. Boy, was I listened to! We were all out within two minutes and safely back in the clinical area. The patient was fine, but we made the decision to keep him overnight in one of our clinic beds. I did not have to return to that bunkbed unit. Shortly after that (4 months), this particular prison was closed because it was so old. Never did I return! The building still stands today, and I will tell you, it makes Shutter Island look like Disney World.

Sean

I had been very busy working in the prison system for about 8 years and very comfortable in my position as a triage nurse manager (one of a few roles) in a busy clinical setting. I would manage huge, long medication lines along with handling emergencies as they came up. I worked primarily 2-10 pm and worked alone most of the time as it was a smaller prison and a one-man show. The MD and Psych Services were around but had usually left soon after my arrival. My backup were the correctional officers who were terrific and always had my back and took very good care of me always. Mind you, there were times I had my disagreements with officers and Sgts, Lt's, Captains, all the way to Dep. Superintendents on occasion, but we all got over it eventually!! It was stressful at times.

Working in a prison was very different than any other place I had worked including Saudi Arabia. Every door had to be locked and double locked. You could never be alone, and your officer had to know what you were up to at all times. They even knew when I was in the bathroom. Sometimes, I would feel angry, but then I would realize that this was only for my safety. Then I would feel so very thankful and grateful that I had such determined young men and women to look after me. And trust me, there were times I needed to be looked after. At the beginning of my tenure, I did not realize that my safety was in such jeopardy, and I was complacent to a fault. Fortunately, it was never truly tested, but I did suddenly realize after hearing stories of other nurses whose lives were in jeopardy. Sadly, with ill effects!

One particular day, a young officer spoke to me in a very harsh tone, and I gave it right back, and only at that time did I realize how correct he was. I stopped talking, and I remember saying, "Greg, you are so right, and I am a big jackass." He was only trying to help me, and I finally got it. I was working in a prison, and no matter how well I knew the inmates, I was still at risk at all times. Never again did an issue come up!! Years flew by with many incidences, both with staff and with inmates. But I did love the job. One particular inmate "Sean" was a very distraught young man (they all were), but he had done so well moving from a high-security prison to a medium-security prison and had integrated well with the general population. He had even found a job in the kitchen and became known as one of the best cooks and bakers.

When I knew "Sean" was on, I would go to the kitchen before general chow time and would be given a delicious baked goodie from him. He would treat us all and always make extra huge cookies that could have been sold at a French bakery for at least a few dollars apiece. I never did pick a favorite inmate, but there were times when certain personalities needed your help more than others, and I would always try within my own boundaries to assist a little extra when I could. "Sean" was one of those inmates. He had a very sad life of abandonment and violence with abuse. So therefore, it was great to see him do so well in such a short amount of time. One particular Sunday eve (my last day before my 18-day vacation), I was organizing and finishing up all my other administration duties, not wanting to leave work for the first shift nurses. I was excited and happy with lots of fun things planned. Nothing could go wrong. But, it did! About 9 pm after the evening medication line, I received a radio call stating that one of the inmates was being brought down for an evaluation (medical and psych). I was wondering who because they never told you for security reasons until the inmate was there in person. I remember walking down to lockup and looking in the room and seeing "Sean", but before I was even there, I could hear the screams and yells with swearing.

I did not recognize the angry voice and was wondering who? And what had happened? The lockup room had a thick metal door with a metal toilet and sink. The inmate was put in there cuffed with hands behind his back with shoes, laces, etc., removed to eliminate suicide. The patient is immediately put on suicide watch until everyone can figure out what is going on. And much to my dismay, it was "Sean"! I barely recognized him. As I was approaching him with 2-3 CO's present (for my safety), my heart just sank. I felt so sad. I have to say it bothered me to see him like this. And I thought he had been doing so well. But, many times, patients in a closed and secure setting can appear alright but can quickly change under duress for any reason. I could not get Sean to focus. I did a medical assessment and psych evaluation and knew that I would have to call both doctors (Mental Health & MD). He was immediately sent to a higher security facility for further evaluation and treatment. By the time I got his charts and meds together for the drivers, it was time for me to report and go home to start my vacation. I felt a little numb leaving a patient in such a curious and bad state and not knowing what the outcome would be. At least I knew he was safe and would receive further treatment. I also remember not sleeping well that night. I did a lot of tossing and turning, trying to figure out what happened and why the change in his condition. The next morning, I still did not feel settled, but had to learn to let go and get on with my own life and vacation. There were other people depending on me with obligations I had made.

Eventually, I did start to enjoy my vacation. When I did return to work, I was hoping that "Sean" had been treated and returned to us. But that was not the case. I had to be careful around my investigation when I returned as the rule of thumb is to never get involved. And I did not want to bring attention to myself. I did find out that he had been transferred to a couple of different places under closer supervision. "Sean" had been put in isolation for his own safety during his treatment process (medical adjustment). He never did return to us. But I can only hope that he found his way out of the system back home and hopefully utilizing his talents.

Tony

Another incident comes to mind. I call this an incident because it was exactly that. It took me over 3 hours to complete the paperwork and documentation both in writing and reports in the computer. I am pretty sure most people realize by now the amount of paperwork and documentation, which is necessary for all RN's. It seems we have less and less time to actually treat and spend time with patients these days. Case in point.... I spent over 10 years working in the prison system, which was under the definition of "Public Health Nursing", part of my job was also work in a clinic as a triage nurse and medication dispenser. I loved this job. I also worked at other correctional facilities to help out on occasion. But my "home" was a medium-security prison which housed lifers, high profile prisoners, and many, which came to us from maximum security, and they were working their way down to minimum then release. The crimes were varied. I will say no more.

Anyway, this was a typical busy evening, and I was about to start my medline. Many times, emergencies came up, and you had to stop the line to take care of the emergency. We had one inmate in a wheelchair. I will call him "Tony". He was not a lifer and was waiting to be released within a two-year period. So, he had some time left. "Tony" came to the medline and usually tried to come at the beginning. His medications were many with narcotic dosing because of his arthritis and bone pain. I did my usual routine, giving him his regular meds first, and it was the responsibility of the Officer to make sure he took them and that they were completely swallowed. Then I would go to our narcotic cabinet and withdraw what was needed, document it in the narcotic book, then give it to him. I handed him the 3 pills (MS Contin), and we would monitor him. I passed the little white cup to him and noticed he was talking to the officer. I then said, "Tony, take your pills." What followed I could not believe. "Hey Miss Kitty, you must have forgotten to put the pills in the cup, Ha HA!" I looked at the officer, and there were no pills in the cup. Somehow, my little quick-fingered patient had somehow ditched them somewhere and wanted more. I stopped the medline, called a "99" emergency (not medical), and all came running. Both the Captain and the Lieutenant searched him and his wheelchair to find nothing. I knew it had to be there, and I was expected to give him an additional dosing which I did not do.

I called the MD on call who took my side, and I was instructed not to give the additional dosing. The inmate/patient was quite upset and was delivered back to his room. But as a result, I was backlogged the rest of the night because of the paper work. Instead of leaving at 10:30 pm, I left after midnight. Not only did I have to call the MD but also the Administrator on call, the nursing supervisor, Mental Health, and created reports for the Captain, Superintendent, and nursing in both the chart and in the computer. This compounded with ugly stares from others for not remedicating this patient who was truly a gifted magician. A couple of weeks later, "Tony" did get caught. Seems he had been hoarding his meds and using his wheelchair as his hiding place. A couple of weeks later, "Tony" got caught while visiting our resident MD.

Tony was up on the exam table and the doctor picked up his wheelchair seat unzipped it, and wow, found a stash of narcotics!! I am never happy to see a person/inmate/patient hit hard times, but this time, I was relieved and happy that he had been caught. He was sent out to another facility of higher security. I am so glad I stuck to my guns because I knew I was right. How could I have possibly forgotten his medication, and the narcotic count was correct. You can never become complacent while working!!

Mike

Did I mention I am a single female? Throughout the years, I will admit I have been approached by several male patients, which I did let down ever so lightly with the use of a white lie. Sometimes, you must create a white lie to save face but also not to hurt anyone's feelings. During my stint working in the prison (10 years), I was running a medical clinic in one of the medium-security prisons. I loved this job because I worked alone and handled emergencies as they arose in a clinic setting. I would replace the 7-3 nurse and work till 3-11. Anything could happen at any time, and I loved the diversity of the job. Which is how I met "Mike" who was prepping for a GI procedure, and I had to deliver this rather foul-tasting liquid for him to drink within 15 minutes. I had to stay with him with an officer present. Just in those 15 minutes, I was struck completely with this man. I felt a very strong connection to him immediately. I can only describe it as someone I once knew. This is how the friendship started. But I did not want to share my friendship with Mike with anyone, as I did not have complete trust with many of my working buddies. Nice people, but people like to talk. Especially the inmates were all people watchers, and nothing got passed most of them. So, I had to be very careful!! I looked forward to going to work just to see Mike. If he walked pass me during rounds, we would always talk. At the medication line, he would be the last one in line, so we could snatch a few extra minutes to "talk".

We talked about everything!! He was a musician, and we were born the same year, and he grew up just a couple of towns over from me. His first wife divorced him after he entered prison because of his lengthy sentence. I will not discuss his case, but I knew and understood all the circumstances surrounding his situation. He had two grown children of which one he was in contact with. I did forget to mention, that he did spend much time at the clinic because of his diagnosis of stomach cancer, which broke my heart. At one point, he was in the hospital for surgery and follow-up chemotherapy. I had not seen him for almost a month. He had to be placed in the prison infirmary after his hospitalization. I made sure I called at least once a week from work to get updates from the other nurses. When I called, I also requested that the officer and the nurse relay a get well greeting from me and the rest of the nurses. Finally, he returned back to his home site (prison), and the news was good. Cancer free!!

Mike had made the decision to not continue with treatment. Myself and his doctors did not agree with this, but he was determined to "beat the cancer on his own". For a while, he did well and gained weight, worked out in the gym, and had a good appetite. Our evening medication line talks continued. When he was ready to walk away from the med counter, he would always put his hand close to the window which I stood behind and gently tap his hand twice and wink. Nobody saw his wink because he was facing me with his head slightly turned.

Within 4 months, the news had changed, and the cancer returned. I was heartbroken as his prognosis was poor. But he was still determined to beat it. I wanted him to receive his treatments, but he did not want to. I realized that I wanted him to get better for selfish reasons. I had to come to the realization that he wanted to let go and let nature take its course. He was up for parole in a couple of years but was not sure if it would pass, as it had been denied in the past. To continue to live his life imprisoned was no longer an option for him. So, I had to let go of him, too. He was eventually transferred to a correctional hospice unit and was declining steadily. I continued with my weekly calls to his unit. I could never speak to him as it was not allowed. He did eventually succumb and died without ever having been paroled.

Getting Laid Off

After working several years in the prison system, I had decided to move around and seek another position within the prison...just felt as though I needed a change. I was about 5 years away from retiring and decided a little change would be good for me for the final 5 years. There were not many available positions to meet my nursing skills, and I had the commute to think about. I was already driving close to 88 miles round trip 4 days per week. I inquired if there was a suitable position but nothing. I applied for a specific Public Health position working with inmates with serious public health issues, but to my dismay, they chose a younger male nurse with many years less experience than myself. I was quite disappointed!!

Soon, it got to be holiday time and not the most convenient time to job hunt in New England with lots of snow. My plan was to wait for the worst of winter to be over, then hit the ground again. About the same time, there were rumblings of lay-offs and re-distribution of jobs among nursing. I thought, how could they! We are always so short-staffed. Within a month, many nurses were laid-off and soon again, 3-4 months later, another group was let go, but I was still at my job. I was utilized to train newer nurses with salary cuts. Once my job was completed, I was let go with unemployment benefits. I never saw it coming!!

Well, I rested a while, had a knee replacement, and was finally ready to seek employment again. By this time, I was over 60 years old but had planned to work to 65. Well, I updated my resume and soon found out that looking for a job was not so easy. I am not computer-savvy and soon found out that applying for a job was a full-time job (on the computer!!). No calling up facilities, or even mailing a resume. Everything is to be done electronically. What a challenge! Sometimes, it would take me 3 hours to fill out one application online. And I would hope and pray that it was received. I had to upload, download, copy and paste, e-mail, etc. I had to take a special course to learn computers. No matter what I did, there was no forthcoming job. I even had phone interviews. When I would finally make it through a door, it was a revolving door in every sense of the term. It appeared to me, that the interviews went very well. I took coaching lessons but something seemed to happen.... I was never hired!! All my computer classes, coaching for interviews, and career assistance did not land me a job.

I was feeling pretty bad about myself and my self-esteem was in the gutter. One particular day, I was at a public health conference and speaking with other nurses. We all exchanged stories about careers. I, of course, shared my dilemma and unemployment status. One very kind hearted soul explained, "It's not you, it's age discrimination. I have been looking for a job for over two years, and I am 5 years younger!" She went on to share with me that there were many more in our ranks. I initially felt relieved that it was possibly age discrimination. But, soon I realized, I would still have a hard time seeking employment and my employment compensation with medical insurance was soon to run out.

Retirement

By the time I had reached my 60's, I decided to retire and see what life had to offer. Much thought went into finances and scrunching of numbers, but I would be able to swing it as long as I chose occasional work. Fortunately, I was able to find occasional work to see me through. There was a small nursing center up the street offering 32 hours a month, which is all I needed. I did completely retire at age 66 and was very happy with my final decision. When I look back to my nursing career and all the wonderful places I worked, I have no regrets. I lived a life of "giving" and "healing".

It has been a beautiful life with rich memories of joy, sadness, sometimes fear, but mostly feelings of WOW. I cannot believe I experienced this. When I look back to my nursing career, and all that it entailed, I feel so incredibly lucky and honored to be part of such an honorable career. Choosing nursing was a decision I made to experience miracles. And that I did!

Saudi Arabia

I decided to save my transcultural nursing experience for the last chapter. I accepted a job in Riyadh, Saudi Arabia (S.A.) after my hemodialysis job and before my Healthcare for the Homeless job in Boston. This last chapter is devoted to S.A.

It took quite a while to find the appropriate job and gather Iqamas (work papers), passports, and of course traveling to Canada for the job interview. Nobody can enter Saudi Arabia, and you must have permission from their government (meaning the king and his princes). Eventually, I made it over there in March of 1990. I did miss my Hemodialysis position in Boston, but this was another adventure I could not let pass by. It was a long and somewhat horrendous flight. 14 hours!! Their human resource (HR) department was there to greet me (King Khalid Hospital) in Riyadh. Only problem was the Airline had lost my luggage. I remember meeting my Supervisor Mishelle, and she was very kind to lend me some clothes. By the way, she was close to 6 feet, and I am barely 5 feet. Shortly other donations did arrive, and my lost luggage was found. King Khalid (KKESH) services the entire middle east for eye conditions and other medical issues. I worked on the Women's unit preparing patients for surgery with post-op care. Women and men are separated at all times except for when they are in their homes. The Saudi women were on the whole very friendly.

A big advantage of working abroad is having the opportunity to work with other medical personnel from around the world. I worked with Americans, Canadians, Irish, English, Scottish, French, Aussies, New

Zealanders, Swedes, Finns, Filipinos, Indians, and a host of others. We all had to speak English. It was a good fit for me, and soon, the months did pass. The hospital was beautiful and had their own compound with swimming pools, tennis courts, walking paths, buses, or limos to take you shopping. Also, sign up events and sightseeing tours! I was always treated very well. Many people have asked me about the strict rules for women, and yes, there are strict rules. But soon after you arrive, you learn to integrate and meet friends and socialize. I was lucky to be invited to many embassy parties.

Before deciding to work in Saudi Arabia or even entering the country, everyone must attend a briefing or informational seminar about the country and its restrictions. It is a 100% Muslim country and places of worship are called Mosques. All Muslims are expected to pray 5 times per day. A very loud whistle will blow to remind you. No other places of worship are allowed in Saudi Arabia. The main Islamic center is in Mecca, and only Muslims are allowed to go there. If you are caught being there, it is punishable with a hefty prison sentence. Depending on where you are living, all women must wear an Abaya (black) coat-like silk, and cover their heads with a scarf. While on the compound, you can wear plain street clothes, but all body parts must be covered. The language is Arabic, which is very difficult, but I was able to pick up many medical terms. No dating, men and women cannot be seen together in public unless married. Because of many of these restrictions, the expats do not have much socialization with the Saudis. Expats are everyone who is not Muslim.

There are many differences throughout the various territories. Such as if you compliment a Saudi woman on something she is wearing, she will remove it and give it to you. It would be a great insult if you did not accept her gift. Saudi Arabia has different terrains such as dry desert with white sand and a red sand desert. There are mountain regions which are mostly stone and some areas look like Utah, USA. Jeddah is on the Red Sea which is very humid. As stated earlier, I was lucky to meet ambassadors and other VIP'S. The embassy parties were in palaces and were quite beautiful. This is where you could drink alcohol, otherwise any form of alcohol was not allowed in the country. Many folks did make their own concoctions, which was not so bad tasting. Another form of entertainment was going on a Hash (nothing to do with the drug) or walk about out in the desert for a picnic. Large groups would form and meet at designated places and drive, then climb and walk and meet new people. There were also private parties to attend (secretly). Most embassies had classical concerts and operas. There were many parties on the compounds, and this is where you could socialize with other middle-easterners.

What comes to mind mostly is the diversity of people getting along and socializing and working well together. On a few occasions, I did meet Ambassadors from other countries. Sorry, I cannot kiss and tell! But among my friends, several relationships did form, with a marriage or two. There was also some fun with the occasional practical joke, but it will not go any further than that. The Scandinavian embassies had hot tubs where you could jump into the hot tub for a while, then jump into the cold one with ice. Invigorating, yes!! (Wearing bathing suits!) So, you are probably wondering did Kitty ever work or just socialize? Yes, I did and very hard. My 2nd year, I was offered the manager's position on my unit, which I accepted. With it came a few extra unusual responsibilities. My unit had the VIP suite as I mentioned. The suite was created for the royal family and other higher up government officials and their families. I was invited to have tea with one of the Princesses, which I accepted. Tea is always offered with dates. The tea is very different as it has a bitter taste and is green.

I was expected to go and someone else had to take over my position for the rest of the day. You cannot refuse because it is considered a big insult to refuse. Her private maids were with her. We all had a grand time chatting and eating. Many of our differences were discussed openly. I, the westerner, questioned why they had to cover up and could not drive. They in turn think western women are prisoners to makeup and fashion and think it is all ridiculous. Some of the women went onto say that they are the bosses in their homes and not the men. Behind closed doors, the Saudi women rule. Outside the home, the men are dominant. All in all, it was a very busy unit. Several times a year usually around Ramadan (their holy month of Islam), the Bedouins would arrive into Riyadh with their camels in tow for medical checkups. Most middle-easterners have severe problems with their eyes because of the hot desert sun. It can burn away their irises, causing their dark brown eyes to turn blue or opaque. These conditions need surgery, and our hospital (KKESH) was responsible for their care.

Shopping was also a great outlet. The shops or Suqs were one of a kind. Saudi Arabia had things you could purchase, which could never be purchased anywhere else. They had gold suqs, antique suqs, carpet suqs, etc. It was an easy trap to get into and spend all your money. My extra cash went into traveling. We had ample time off, and I used it well. I will name the countries I visited, starting with a safari in Kenya, a second safari in Kenya, Zimbabwe, and Botswana, and Egypt with a cruise down the Nile with all the sightseeing. At that time, tourists were allowed to climb into the second pyramid to the top, which I did. Also, I went to Singapore, Hong Kong, Malaysia, then onto China and all its beauty and sites, including climbing the Great Wall of China and visiting the Winter and Summer Palaces.

On my trip back from the Far East, I stopped in Bahrain, then back to Riyadh. After the Gulf war, I went to Syria, which has lots to see and do. Traveling through Damascus is like stepping back in time about 1000 years. I remember walking down the street called Strait, which I believe is mentioned in the Bible and sitting under St. Paul's window, meditating for a while. I was in two countries at a same time. The Border Patrol in Syria allowed us to put one foot in Iraq and keep the other foot in Syria. We all had a good laugh!! It saddens me when I think of all the wars and destruction. While living in Saudi Arabia, there are many sites to see as well. You must be with a guide at all times. If you like the ocean, you can take a quick flight to Jeddah, which is on the Red Sea. We snorkeled and saw some of the Coral Reef, which was beautiful. The climate is different in some areas. It is very humid in Jeddah. Medina with all its ancient history (cities build of stone in caves), and Cleopatra's actual birth place. We viewed the train and tracks where Lawrence of Arabia traveled through. It was also very cheap to fly to Dubai for a long weekend. The food and shopping while visiting and swimming in the Indian ocean was a nice get-away.

Living in Saudi Arabia – Gulf War

I knew I could not finish my book without mentioning the Gulf War. I remember very clearly on a Friday afternoon in August 1990. I was at the compound's swimming pool. None of us knew our lives would change so quickly and without notice. A woman came out of the locker room screaming, "Iraq has just invaded Kuwait". We were all stunned and were hoping she received the message incorrectly. Riyadh is just under 200 miles from Kuwait City. We all left the pool, went to our homes, and turned on our TV's. I was especially concerned because 3 Filipino nurses I worked with had flown to Kuwait City to take their nursing boards.

Everything was at a standstill for a very long time. The surrounding countries were closed down, and only VIP flights left the Riyadh Airport. My immediate concern were the three nurses in Kuwait. There was no or very little communication from anywhere in that area. Iraq had completely toppled the computer and communication system. Kuwait was down. We had no way of reaching the nurses over there, and they could not contact us. There were many upsetting messages from the girls' families, but we had no way of reaching them.

Finally, within a week, there was some communication, and they were allowed to leave Kuwait. They were locked in their hotel rooms for several days and heard many shots being fired with expired bodies in the hotel fountain. Fortunately, they arrived back safely, unharmed. That was just the beginning. Over the next several months, there was a huge military buildup in Saudi Arabia and Riyadh. This was done to keep Kuwait safe. The coalition military arrived from the US, England, Ireland, Germany, France, Scandinavia, Australia, New Zealand, and probably other countries, too.

Most of the westerners stayed, but there were some that left. It was difficult to leave because the air space was shut off. If you were lucky enough to get a flight out, you had to take a helicopter out to a specified place, then onto a military airport in a military plane. I stayed! There were a few nurses who had nervous breakdowns and were sent home via the military after treatment. It was rough going because we did not know what Saddam was going to do. It was nerve wracking waiting to have a war start because we had no idea when. The phone calls from home were so hard to take with lots of tears at times.

In January of 1991, we were ready for what we did not know. Everyone on the compound was fitted for gas masks. We did not know what Saddam would be sending us via air strike. But instead, it was a missile. We heard the first air raid during mid-day on a Saturday. I remember thinking that it sounded just like the ones you hear on TV in WW2 movies. When you are stressed, you think of strange things.... anything to occupy your mind. I remember sitting in my apartment with the mask on and waiting for an explosion. There were many explosions. However, our Patriot missiles intercepted them!! These attacks went on and off for two months. One night, England and America sent planes to bomb Iraq. I remember hearing the super loud rumbling. I did not know that when military planes attack, many times they fly closer to the ground.

I think it were the planes which upset me the most. That was the one noise and vision I will never forget. So close.... During this time, I did have an opportunity to meet many of the military reporters from the news stations. By this time, things did open up a little. It was surreal for a while walking around downtown Riyadh with military from all over the world. Everyone was scared and concerned but friendly. Finally, things did quiet down, and the military stayed for a while. I never thought I would experience an active war during my transcultural nursing experience. I am not in the military and never was. I did learn a lot during my nursing school years but never how to handle oneself during a war halfway around the world. After 3 years, I returned home to the great USA (1993).

To this day, many of us are still in touch. Living and working abroad was a huge benefit. Presently, I feel saddened our country's relationship is strained, but will continue to pray for a peaceful outcome for all.

Other Opportunities

Since I like to travel, I researched and found other avenues of education with travel and site seeing. I traveled with Professional Medical Conferences – a company that will send groups of medical professionals to other countries to learn and meet others at their workplaces in a conference setting. Ideas are exchanged, and topics are discussed, like who receives care? How is it delivered? And who or how is it paid for? I was very lucky to visit Ireland, Swaziland (Eswatini) and South Africa. On Off time site seeing tours are arranged. In Swaziland (2006), their king was a very "hands-on leader". His children did help out their country by working various jobs to keep the economy growing. I was told that you can identify a member of the Royal Family because they wear a red feather on their head while they work. The morning I left, I heard a knock on my hotel door. And standing in front of me was a native in full dress wearing a red feather to collect my luggage!! As it turns out, he was a Prince and the direct son of the King!! Many of these experiences were surreal.

Made in the USA
Coppell, TX
20 April 2024